T4-AVA-250

Hopscotch Daydream

by Scott Ryan

illustrated by Alexandra Wallner

Hope looks at the new painting. She sees kids from long ago playing. "It looks fun," says Hope.

Then Hope finds June and Liz.

"Let's play," says Hope.

Hope, June, and Liz get to work. They make a hopscotch game. Soon they are done.

"Let's play," says Hope.

Hope throws a stone.
She hops to the end.

Hope looks up and sees kids playing. They look like the kids in the painting. Hope does, too.

The kids are playing an old game.

What a funny daydream!

"Hope! Hope!" calls June.

"Time to hop back!"
says Liz.

Hope hops back.

"Why did you stop?"
Liz asks.

Hope tells them about her daydream.

"How fun!" says Liz.

Hope goes home after the game. She tells Mom and Dad about her daydream.

"How fun!" they say.

Comprehension Check

Retell the Story

Use a Draw Conclusions Chart. Tell what happens in the story that helps you draw a conclusion.

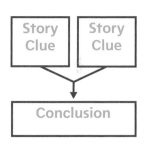

Think and Compare

1. What does Hope like about the new painting?

2. Have you ever seen a painting that you liked? What did you like about it?

3. Why do people like to look at paintings?